BASIC/NOT BORING
MATH SKILLS

PROBLEM
SOLVING

Grades 4-5

Inventive Exercises to Sharpen
Skills and Raise Achievement

Series Concept & Development
by Imogene Forte & Marjorie Frank

Exercises by Charlotte Poulos

Illustrations by Kathleen Bullock

Incentive Publications, Inc.
Nashville, Tennessee

About the cover:
Bound resist, or tie dye, is the most ancient known method
of fabric surface design. The brilliance of the basic tie dye
design on this cover reflects the possibilities that emerge
from the mastery of basic skills.

Cover art by Mary Patricia Deprez, dba Tye Dye Mary®
Cover design by Marta Drayton, Joe Shibley, and W. Paul Nance
Edited by Tama Montgomery

ISBN 0-86530-405-X

PRINTED IN THE UNITED STATES OF AMERICA

TABLE OF CONTENTS

CELEBRATE BASIC MATH SKILLS

Basic does not mean boring! There is certainly nothing dull about . . .
 . . . calculating hockey injuries or kayak dunkings in a wild river
 . . . learning about great snowboard tricks like Fakies, Wheelies, and McTwists
 . . . following mountain climbers as they slip and slide up and down the slopes
 . . . looking in on a burly weight lifter as he mixes up a power drink for his friends
 . . . finding out the weight of a sumo wrestler or the number of dimples on a golf ball
 . . . using numbers to help out surfers, scuba divers, or speed skaters
 . . . figuring out who has done the most flips on the trampoline

These are just some of the adventures students will explore as they celebrate basic problem-solving skills. The idea of celebrating the basics is just what it sounds like—sharpening math skills while enjoying the fun of sports teams and events. Each page invites learners to try a high-interest, visually appealing math exercise built around sports situations. This is not just an ordinary fill-in-the-blanks way to learn. These exercises are fun and surprising, and they make good use of thinking skills. Students will do the useful work of practicing a specific problem-solving skill or strategy while stepping into the fascinating world of individual and team sports.

The pages in this book can be used in many ways:
  • for individual students to review or practice a particular skill
  • to sharpen the skill with a small or large group
  • by students working on their own
  • by students working under the direction of an adult

Each page may be used to introduce a new skill, reinforce a skill, or assess a student's ability to perform a skill. And there's more than just the great student activity pages. You'll also find an appendix filled with resources for students and teachers—including a ready-to-use test for assessing problem-solving skills.

As your students take on the challenges of these adventures with problem solving, they will grow! And as you watch them check off the basic math skills they've strengthened, you can celebrate with them!

The Skills Test
Use the skills test beginning on page 56 as a pretest and/or a post-test. This will help you check the students' mastery of problem-solving skills and strategies and will prepare them for success on achievement tests.

SKILLS CHECKLIST FOR
PROBLEM SOLVING, Grades 4-5

✔	SKILL	PAGE(S)
	Solve a variety of word problems	10–17, 19–21, 25, 27–30, 34–50
	Identify information needed for solving a problem	10–13
	Solve problems involving U.S. Customary measurements	10, 11, 22
	Solve problems involving metric measurements	10, 11, 23
	Solve problems using fractions	10, 11, 24
	Solve problems using decimals	10, 11, 25, 28, 29
	Identify information that may be missing from a problem	12
	Eliminate excess information	13
	Solve problems using information from diagrams and illustrations	15, 20–23, 28, 31, 32, 37, 39, 42, 43
	Choose correct equations to solve problems	16
	Translate problems into equations	16, 17
	Find solutions to equations	16, 17
	Solve problems using information from charts, graphs, and tables	18, 19, 27, 44
	Solve multistep problems	21, 26–30, 33, 36, 37, 42–44
	Solve problems using statistical data	18, 19, 37, 44
	Find missing numbers for problem solutions	27
	Solve problems using money	28, 29, 37
	Select appropriate operation(s) for solving problems	30, 31
	Use formulas to find perimeter, area, and volume of geometric figures	32, 33
	Solve problems involving ratios	34
	Solve problems involving percent	34, 35, 37
	Solve problems involving time	36
	Solve consumer problems involving taxes and discounts	37
	Use estimation to solve problems	38, 46, 47
	Create diagrams, models, or charts to help solve problems	39
	Use mental math to solve problems	40, 41, 46–48
	Use logic to solve problems	42, 43
	Find more than one solution to a problem	44, 45
	Choose an appropriate strategy to solve a given problem	46, 47
	Write explanations of how problems were solved	48, 49
	Check the accuracy of problem solutions	50

PROBLEM SOLVING

Skills Exercises

WINTER SPORTS FEST

Every winter the Bigtown Middle School has a big Winter Sports Fest. Students can take part in all kinds of sports—from ski races and ice carving contests to elaborate snowball throwing competitions. To solve the problems about this event, you will have to decide which pieces of information are needed. For each problem on pages 10 and 11, circle the letters of the information items that are needed to find the answer. Solve the problems on a separate piece of paper, and write the answers after each problem.

1. How many cups of hot chocolate did the skaters drink? _____

   a. 500 cups of hot chocolate were gulped or sipped by all the students this year.
   b. 40 cups were drunk by the sledders and the skiers.
   c. The ice skaters drank $\frac{1}{10}$ of the hot chocolate.

2. What is Jenny's record distance for a snowball throw? _____

   a. Jenny's snowball was $2\frac{1}{2}$ inches in diameter.
   b. Joe's snowball was 3 inches in diameter.
   c. Jenny's record distance for a snowball throw is 6 meters farther than Joe's.
   d. Joe's record throw is 58.4 meters.

3. What was the difference between the highest and lowest temperatures during the 1998 Winter Sports Fest? _____

   a. On the warmest day of the 1998 Winter Sports Fest, the highest temperature was 31°F.
   b. Water freezes at 32°F.
   c. The coldest temperature during the 1998 Sports Fest was 18°F.
   d. The wind blew at 21 mph.
   e. The lowest temperature in 1996 was −6°F.

4. How many spectators watched the events in the afternoon? _____

   a. There were 196 spectators attending before noon.
   b. The crowd dwindled to 53 at lunchtime.
   c. The crowd in the afternoon was $1\frac{1}{2}$ times the size of the morning crowd.

Use with page 11.

Name

5. How much faster than Wanda and Will were the sled run winners? _____

    a. Water freezes at 32°F.
    b. Wanda and Will finished the sledding run in 1 minute 22 seconds.
    c. The slowest sled run time was 1 minute 41 seconds.
    d. Erin and Erika won the sled race with a time of 1 minute 15 seconds.
    e. The slowest sled run was 26 seconds longer than the fastest time.

6. About how many snowballs did each kid throw? _____

    a. 704 snowballs were thrown during the snowball fight competition.
    b. There were 16 kids on each of two teams.
    c. There was an equal number of fourth graders on each team.

7. What fraction of the ski team wore goggles? _____

    a. The ski team had 30 members.
    b. $\frac{1}{5}$ of the team members wore sunglasses.
    c. There were 16 girls and 14 boys on the team.
    d. 25 of the kids on the team wore goggles.

8. How many fewer times did the 6th graders fall than the 8th graders? _____

    a. There were 74 falls on the 7th-grade snowboard team.
    b. There were 88 falls on the 8th-grade snowboard team.
    c. There were 50 falls on the 6th-grade team.
    d. There were 7 members on the 8th-grade team.

9. Who was the fastest of the three racers, and what was his or her time? _____

    a. The speed skating competition was for a 500-meter distance.
    b. Sara skated the race in 65 seconds.
    c. James took 5 seconds longer than Sara.
    d. Barry's race time was 2 seconds faster than Sara's.

10. How many awards were given all together? _____

    a. The trophies and medals were awarded at the end of the Sports Fest.
    b. Awards were given for 28 events.
    c. Four awards were given for each event.
    d. Speed skaters won 16 of the awards.

Use with page 10.

Name _____

SOMETHING'S MISSING!

When Suzie heads down the slalom slopes, it's hard to get her to stop—even though she is missing something important for her race! Something is also missing in each of these problems. For each problem, tell what other facts are needed to find the answer.

Something's missing...

1. The wind at the top of Suzie's run is 26 mph. She skis down the mountain at 38 mph. How much faster is the wind blowing at the top of the run than at the bottom?

   _____

2. There are 4,866 skiers on the slopes at Holiday Hollow today. Some are intermediate and expert skiers, and $\frac{1}{5}$ of them are beginners. How many are expert skiers?

   _____

3. New skier, Abigail, fell 17 times during the first hour of her lesson. She fell twice that many times during the second hour. How many times did she fall all together during her 3-hour lesson? _____

4. Last week, 1,700 ski passes were sold. In previous weeks, 7,100 were sold. How many more were sold this season than last? _____

5. Suzie spent $139 for her new ski jacket and $520 for her new skis. How much more did the skis cost than the boots? _____

6. Suzie brought $28 for lunches during her ski trip. How much would she be able to spend each day? _____

7. The ski patrol rescues many skiers in trouble each day. Of those, 15% have broken bones. How many broken bones are there a day? _____

8. Anthony has won 7 major slalom races this year. Scott has won 4. Thomas has won twice as many as Will. How many have the four boys won all together? _____

9. Last night 15 inches of new snow fell on the ski hill. How much snow does the ski hill have now? _____

10. There were half as many collisions on the ski hill today as there were on Tuesday, and twice as many as on Monday. How many collisions were there today?

    _____

Name _____

MORE THAN ENOUGH

Wild Will has given a lot more information about his favorite snowboard tricks than is really needed to solve these problems. Cross out the information in each problem that is not needed for the solution. Then, solve the problems.

1. What a great day I had today! This is the 14th competition I've won this year. I won 13 last year with my new $700 snowboard. Today is my 14th birthday, too! How many competitions have I won in the past two years? _____

2. I impressed the crowd with my tricks today. My first run included 4 Tail Grabs and twice as many Tail Rolls. I did 17 tricks in all, including 3 Flips. How many of the tricks were not Tail Grabs or Tail Rolls? _____

3. My last run down the hill took 3 minutes 20.21 seconds. This was 0.33 seconds faster than my first run. I did 3 Backscratchers, 2 Iguana Back Flips, and 5 Nose Rolls. How fast was my first run? _____

4. This season, I've done 200 Ollies and 400 Fakies in practice. I've practiced my McTwist 12 times more than my Fakies. How many McTwists have I done in practice? _____

5. I have practiced my tricks a total of 246 hours so far this season. I've been at the snowboarding park 82 times. It takes 45 minutes to get to the park from my home. My season pass cost $350. About how many hours did I snowboard each time I went to the park? _____

6. This year, 1,200 snowboarders each bought a pass for $350. Anyone under 12 got a 10% discount. There were 180 boarders under 12. There were 70 boarders over 16 who bought passes. How much did the passes cost for kids under 12? _____

7. Julia said she'd take me to a movie if I could do more Slob Airs than she did (without falling). The movie tickets cost $6.50 each. She did 17 Slob Airs without falling. I did 3 times as many as that, but I fell 39 times. Did she have to take me to the movie? _____

8. I fall about 4 times for every 200 feet I snowboard. I have 37 bruises on my body, 6 cuts on my face, and 1 broken finger. If I cover 13,000 feet a week on my snowboard, about how many times will I fall? _____

9. I ate 6 tacos, 2 hot dogs, and 4 energy bars today. I've eaten 9 dozen energy bars this season. How many energy bars did I eat before today? _____

Name _____

SPORTS TRIVIA

Solve these problems and learn some fun sports facts that you can use to impress your friends! Surprise them with your knowledge of sports trivia!

1. Yuki the sumo wrestler loves to eat ice cream before he wrestles. From January to November, he ate 19 kg of ice cream every month. In December, he ate only 16 kg. How many kg did he eat last year?

   _____ kg
   (the average weight of a sumo wrestler)

2. Mac the weightlifter packed his duffel bag carefully. He weighed each item: black belt—8 lb, spandex suit—1 lb, liniment—3 lb, protein powder—9 lb, and an old trophy—23 lb. How much does the stuff in the bag weigh?

   _____ lb
   (weight of a lifting bar)

3. Lincoln and Jefferson Middle Schools had a basketball shoot-out marathon. The Lincoln students made 920 baskets. The Jefferson kids shot 971. How many baskets were made in all?

   _____
   (the year basketball was invented)

4. Keri entered 4 events at the gymnastics meet. She won 1 medal. Her 3 teammates each won 3 medals. How many medals did the whole team win?

   _____
   (the width in centimeters of a balance beam)

Mmmm

5. Juan's swim team swims laps in a small pool. The coach counts every two lengths as 1 lap. If Juan swims 30 lengths, how many laps has he gone?

   _____
   (number of colored balls in a billiards game)

6. Jason is 14 holes short of finishing his 22nd golf game this month. He plays 18 holes during each game. How many holes has he played this month?

   _____
   (the number of dimples on a golf ball)

7. The Philly Freeze hockey team lost $\frac{1}{3}$ of their games last season. They played 9 games. How many did they lose?

   _____
   (the number of points in a hockey "hat trick")

8. The state track meet was held at Feeble Stadium. It holds 12,000 spectators in 4 equal sections of seats. How many fans will fit into each section?

   _____
   (number of meters in a cross-country race)

Name _____

14

LOST IN THE TREES

For this sport, equipment is everything! What is this important piece of equipment? Find out by solving the problems in your head or on a separate piece of paper. Then find the space in the puzzle with the correct answer and color that space with the color given.

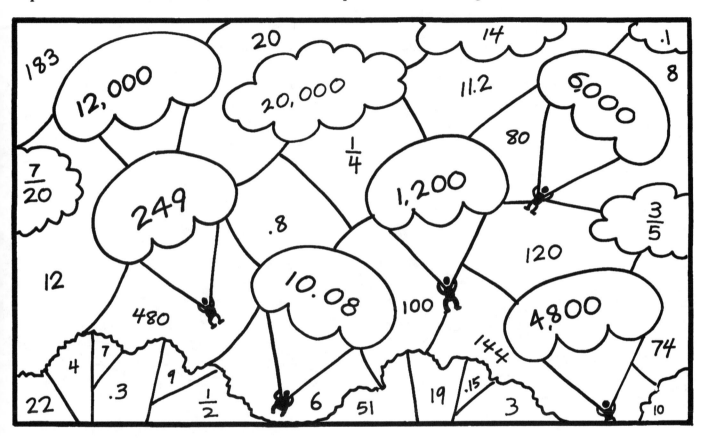

Blue
1. seventeen less than two hundred
2. twenty-one more than fifty-three
3. one-eighth of sixty-four
4. ten squared
5. half of one-half
6. ten times forty-eight
7. half of one hundred sixty
8. twelve dozen

Red
9. twice six thousand
10. ten and eight-hundredths

White
11. $\frac{1}{20}$ less than $\frac{8}{20}$
12. one hundred times two hundred
13. $\frac{1}{2}$ of twenty-eight
14. one minus nine-tenths
15. one minus $\frac{2}{5}$

Yellow
16. five hundred dozen
17. fifty-one less than three hundred

Purple
18. seventy more than fifty
19. two-tenths plus six-tenths

20. greatest common factor of eighteen and twelve
21. least common multiple of three and four
22. least common denominator of $\frac{1}{4}$ and $\frac{7}{10}$
23. twelve minus eight-tenths

Orange
24. four hundred tripled
25. one hundred times forty-eight

Green
All spaces with other answers.

Name

Basic Skills/Problem Solving 4-5

WILD WHITEWATER WHIRL

Kayakers will have a much better chance of getting down wild rivers safely if they choose the best path. You'll have a better chance of solving math problems correctly if you can find the equation that best fits the problem. Circle the correct equation and solve each problem. If you get them right, you'll help Will find the right path down the river.

1. Will puts his kayak in at the dam. The first set of rapids is 3 miles downstream, the next is 4 miles farther, and the next is $2\frac{1}{2}$ miles farther. He gets out 2 miles after the third set. How many miles has he paddled? _____
   a. $3 + 4 = n$
   b. $n = 3 + 4 + 2\frac{1}{2}$
   c. $3 + 4 + 2\frac{1}{2} + 2 = n$
   d. $3 \times 2 \times 2 \times 2\frac{1}{2} = n$

2. It takes 6 hours to drive to Raging River without stopping. If Wanda and Will stop twice for $\frac{1}{2}$ hour each time and once for a 1-hour lunch, how long will their trip take? _____
   a. $n = 6 + \frac{1}{2} + \frac{1}{2}$
   b. $n = 6 + \frac{1}{2} - \frac{1}{2} + 1$
   c. $6 + \frac{1}{2} + \frac{1}{2} + 1 = n$
   d. $6 - \frac{1}{2} - \frac{1}{2} - 1 = n$

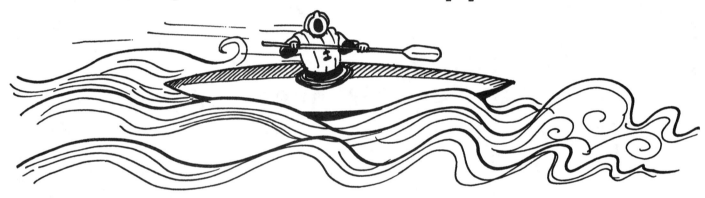

3. Will and his 12 teammates each have a helmet, paddle, wetsuit, and splashskirt to carry in their kayaks. How many items of gear do they have in all? _____
   a. $12 \times 4 = n$
   b. $n = 4 \times 13$
   c. $12 + 4 = n$
   d. $1 + 1 + 1 + 1 + 12 = n$

4. This summer Will entered 17 whitewater rodeos. This was 9 more than last year. How many rodeos did he enter last year?

   _____
   a. $17 + 9 = n$
   b. $n = 17 \times 9$
   c. $n = 17 - 9$
   d. $17 \div 9 = n$

5. The Whitewater club has 24 members with kayaks. If each car-top rack holds 4 kayaks, how many cars will they need to travel? _____
   a. $n = 24 \div 4$
   b. $n = 24 \times 4$
   c. $24 + 4 = n$
   d. $24 - 4 = n$

6. Will got dunked 5 times. Wanda got dunked 3 times. Wayne got dunked twice the number of times that Will and Wanda did. How many times did Wayne go in? _____
   a. $n = 2 (5 + 3)$
   b. $n = 2 + 8 + 3$
   c. $2 \times 5 + 3 = n$
   d. $5 + 3 + 2 \times 5 = n$

Name _____

SINK THAT BASKET

The Panthers and the Warriors are big rivals. This game is the big one! The championship is at stake. To solve these problems about the teams and the game, change each problem into an equation. Read the problem, write an equation, and then solve the equation to find the answer.

1. The Warriors scored 42 two-point baskets and 7 three-pointers. What was their final score?

   _____

2. In this game and the last two games, the Panthers scored the exact same number of points. The total of all these was 216. What was their score for each game?

   _____

3. To get to the game, the Panthers traveled 195 miles less than the Warriors, who traveled 400 miles. How far did the Panthers travel to the game?

   _____

4. The Warriors bought 96 pairs of court shoes at the beginning of the season. They had to buy 28 more a month later to replace the ones that had worn out. How many did they **not** have to replace?

   _____

5. A typical player breathes seven quarts of air a minute while sitting on the bench and 20 times that much per minute while playing a strenuous game. How many quarts per minute would that be?

   _____

6. There were 155 more Panther fans than Warrior fans at the game. There were 2,224 Warrior fans. Among all of the fans, 350 had to stand. How many fans had seats?

   _____

7. The concession stand took in $4,500 at the game. Of that, $1,850 was for food, and $570 was for souvenirs. The rest was for drinks. How much was spent on drinks?

   _____

8. Player Sarah Peters dribbled the basketball a total distance of 4,788.5 feet. Her sister Denise dribbled it half that far. How far did Denise dribble the ball?

   _____

Name

A SLIPPERY SLOPE

The climbing team is having some trouble this week. On an expedition to the top of Mount Slick, the climbers are finding the slopes to be very slippery. Each day they make progress upward, but on many steps they slide backward. Look at the record of each climber's progress over 3 days. For each one, tell how far they've moved up the mountain by the end of day 3.

Climber	DAY 1		DAY 2		DAY 3		Total
	Feet Up	Feet Slipped Back	Feet Up	Feet Slipped Back	Feet Up	Feet Slipped Back	Feet Gained
Jose	1,295	416	1,001	227	1,720	173	
Abby	1,510	307	1,421	196	1,666	214	
Dylan	2,103	519	1,933	225	1,166	197	
Jessica	1,111	87	1,609	210	2,100	414	
Ryan	1,794	360	1,510	314	1,987	121	
Brad	1,600	765	1,799	201	2,206	316	
Lauren	2,166	409	1,995	179	1,611	209	
Andy	1,618	399	1,816	533	1,159	166	
Alexa	1,999	255	2,030	485	2,000	289	
Denise	1,277	310	1,909	79	1,683	110	

1. Which climber has gotten the farthest?_____

2. If the total climb is 5,000 feet, has any climber reached the top? _____

Name

18

GOAL OR NOT?

Some of the attempts the Bay City Blues soccer players make to score a goal end up being only attempts. Other attempts end up with a goal! Read the graph to find out how many of the attempts are successful. Use the information on the graph to answer the questions.

1. Tess scored goals on what percent of her attempts? _____%
   How many goals did she make? _____

2. Who scored the most goals for the season? _____
   Who was next? _____

3. What was the difference between the number of Patti's attempts and the number of her goals? _____

4. What was the total number of goals the Blues scored for the season? _____

5. Who made the least goals for the season? _____ How many goals did she make? _____

6. What was the total number of attempts for the season? _____

7. Write a fraction that shows the total goals compared to the total attempts for the team. ____

8. Who scored on $\frac{9}{10}$ of her attempts? _____

9. What fraction shows the ratio of Carla's goals to her attempts? _____

10. Who made $\frac{2}{19}$ of the total goals? _____

11. Which players made over 50% of the goals they attempted?

    _____

    _____

12. Which two players together made exactly 50% of the total goals for the season?

    _____

    _____

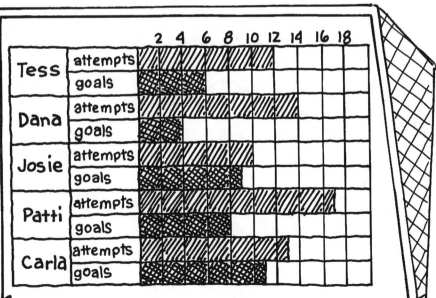

TUGGING PROBLEMS

Take a close look at the team members in this tug-of-war game, so that you can finish the picture accurately. After you have worked each problem, fill in the blank next to it with the number of things you colored or drew.

1. Draw muscles on 10% of the team members. _____

2. Color 0.25 of the girls' hair orange. _____

3. Color 50% of the flowers yellow. _____

4. Color 75% of the hats green. _____

5. Color $\frac{7}{20}$ of the shoes red. _____

6. Color 0.1 of the shoes blue. _____

7. Color $\frac{4}{9}$ of the shirts blue. _____

8. Color $\frac{10}{20}$ of the rope red. _____

9. Draw stars on $\frac{2}{18}$ of the shirts. _____

10. Color 60% of the socks purple. _____

11. Color 0.6 of the shorts orange. ___

12. Draw stripes on $\frac{1}{9}$ of the shirts. _____

13. Color 0.5 of the long pants brown. _____

14. Color bruises on 5% of the elbows. _____

15. Draw bandages on 15% of the knees. _____

16. Put a new hat on 0.1 of the team members. _____

17. Draw mud under $\frac{4}{5}$ of the team members. _____

18. Draw bees stinging 0.2 of the team members. _____

19. Draw untied shoelaces hanging off $\frac{15}{100}$ of the shoes. _____

20. Draw a dog pulling on the shirt of $\frac{10}{100}$ of the team members. _____

Name

RAH, RAH, RAH!

The Slicksville Sluggers' fans are all wound up today. Their team is on a 20-game winning streak! Solve their baseball game problems. Be sure to pay close attention! These problems will take more than one step to solve.

1. Bud, the hot dog vendor, sells 2 sizes of dogs. At Friday's game he sold 14 junior dogs at $1.50 each and 56 jumbo dogs at $2.00 each. How much money did he bring in?

_____

2. Red McGrew had a great game on Saturday. He hit a single, a double, and a home run. If the bases are 90 feet apart, how far did he run on his own hits?

_____

3. Loki's grandpa took his family to the game today. He started with $50. He bought a senior ticket for $5, two adult tickets for $7 each, and four children's tickets at $2.50 each. How much money was left for snacks?

_____

4. It rained at yesterday's game. Luckily, Rosa had brought 3 umbrellas, 2 slickers, and a plastic garbage bag. If 3 can stay dry under each umbrella, how many friends can she help out?

_____

5. Sadie and her 18 friends all wanted to sit together in the bleachers. They found 2 rows with 4 seats each and 2 rows with 3 seats each. How many more seats will they need to find?

_____

6. The booster club sells programs at 20 home games. They need to raise $6,400 for a new scoreboard. At $4 a program, how many will they need to sell at each game?

_____

Name _____

JUST IN CASE

Just in case anyone has wondered about Mochaville Middle School's athletic abilities, the proof of their excellence can be found in the school trophy case. Just step into the lobby of the gym and take a look. Look closely at these trophies! Each one holds a measurement. Several pairs of trophies have measurements that stand for the same amount. Choose 10 different colors of markers or crayons. Color the pairs of matching measurements with the same color.

Name _____

AMAZING FEET

Athletes do amazing things with their feet, and they wear all kinds of interesting footwear while they do these feats. Find the length (in centimeters) of each of these feet (in the shoes or other coverings they wear for their sport). Measure carefully, and pay attention to this scale: 1 centimeter in the picture = 6 centimeters on the real footwear.

Write your answer next to each picture.

1 cm = 6 cm

1.
2.
3.
4.
5.
6.
7.
8.
9.
10.
11.

Name

BRUNO'S BURLY BREW

Big Bruno makes energy shakes for all his weight-lifting pals. One batch makes enough for 4 big weight lifters. Follow the directions to change the recipe for different groups of his friends. (You'll have to multiply some fractions and mixed numerals to do this.)

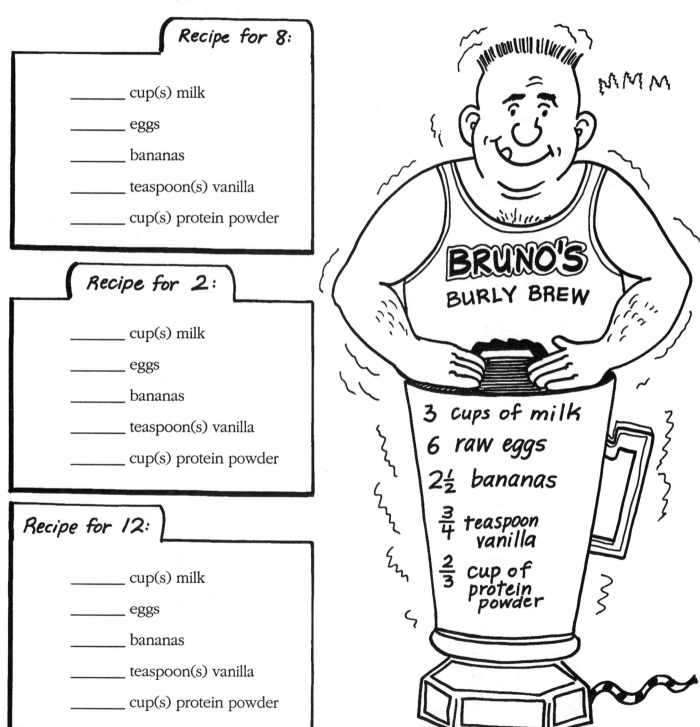

Recipe for 8:

_____ cup(s) milk

_____ eggs

_____ bananas

_____ teaspoon(s) vanilla

_____ cup(s) protein powder

Recipe for 2:

_____ cup(s) milk

_____ eggs

_____ bananas

_____ teaspoon(s) vanilla

_____ cup(s) protein powder

Recipe for 12:

_____ cup(s) milk

_____ eggs

_____ bananas

_____ teaspoon(s) vanilla

_____ cup(s) protein powder

3 cups of milk
6 raw eggs
$2\frac{1}{2}$ bananas
$\frac{3}{4}$ teaspoon vanilla
$\frac{2}{3}$ cup of protein powder

Name _____

24

"FIGURING" OUT DECIMALS

Tamara is working on perfecting her figures for a skating competition. They must be precise for the judges. Numbers with decimals can be tricky, too. You can practice decimals by finding the decimal number in Jenny's figure 8 that matches the problem. Circle each one with the correct color.

_____ 1. one-tenth more than 7 RED

_____ 2. five-hundredths more than 6.3 BLUE

_____ 3. the difference between 10.8 and 10.2 PINK

_____ 4. one hundred plus twelve-hundredths BLACK

_____ 5. 3 tenths more than 6 hundredths YELLOW

_____ 6. 0.05 plus 0.04 PURPLE

_____ 7. 9 tenths less than ten TAN

_____ 8. two-tenths more than 14 ORANGE

_____ 9. 5 hundredths more than 2 BROWN

_____ 10. one-tenth less than one TAN

_____ 11. two-tenths plus four-hundredths SILVER

_____ 12. 9 tenths plus 9 hundredths GREEN

_____ 13. ten plus twelve-hundredths RED

_____ 14. eight-hundredths more than eight BLUE

_____ 15. one-tenth less than ten GREEN

_____ 16. two-tenths less than nine PINK

_____ 17. ten less than 12.4 PURPLE

_____ 18. 0.004 more than 0.005 RED

_____ 19. ten less than 10.22 ORANGE

_____ 20. 0.6 more than three YELLOW

_____ 21. two-tenths more than 0.3 BLUE

_____ 22. 5 tenths less than fifty-one GREEN

_____ 23. five-tenths less than 21 SILVER

_____ 24. one hundred plus two-tenths PURPLE

Numbers in top circle: 0.24 6.35 3.6 9.9 9.1 0.6 8.8 7.1 2.4 2.05 20.5 100.12

Numbers in bottom circle: 0.36 0.22 0.009 14.2 0.09 9.1 100.2 0.9 0.5 3.62 50.5 8.08 10.12 0.99

Name _____

Basic Skills/Problem Solving 4-5

FLIPPING OVER NUMBERS

The Baker kids have been having a great time doing flips on their backyard trampoline. In order to keep track of everyone's total flips, Biff made a chart. By mistake, he left out some numbers. Finish the chart and answer the questions.

	Front Flips	Back Flips	Straddle Flips	Twist Flips	Totals
Biff	4		3	7	18
Bob	2	8	4	4	
Ben		1	6	10	22
BUD	3		3	3	12
Barb	7	9	1	1	
Bonnie	8	6		7	21
Totals					

1. Total Front Flips? _____

2. Who did the most flips? _____

3. Three kids who tied? _____

   _____ _____

4. Who did the most Front Flips? _____

5. Who did the least Straddle Flips? _____

6. Who did the same number of all four kinds of flips? _____

7. Who did the most Twist Flips? _____

8. Who tied in Twist Flips? _____

9. Kind of flip done most? _____

10. Kind of flip done least? _____

11. Barb's most successful flip? _____

12. Bonnie's least successful flip? _____

13. Whose total was 10 more than Bud's? _____

14. What flip total was $\frac{1}{3}$ of Bonnie's total flips? _____

15. Who flipped 3 more than Barb? _____

16. Total of all flips? _____

Name _____

THE MISSING SNACKS

MMMM

Oops! Twelve people walked away from the snack stand without one of the snacks for which they had paid. Which snack is missing? You should be able to tell from looking at the total bill what food item or items they've left behind!

Write the name of the missing food (or souvenir) in the blank for each problem.

Hey! You forgot your change!

HOT DOGS $1.00	ICE CREAM $1.25
HOT PRETZELS.......... 65¢	PIZZA $2.00
DRINKS ....90¢	LICORICE ....30¢
CANDY.................50¢	NACHOS $1.30
POPCORN................60¢	COFFEE ....75¢
PENNANTS..............20¢	HOT CHOCOLATE......80¢

1. 1 hot dog _____
1 drink _____
1 _____ _____
Total $3.90

2. 1 pizza _____
2 _____ _____
1 nachos _____
Total $4.80

3. 1 _____ _____
1 hot chocolate _____
1 popcorn _____
Total $2.65

4. 1 _____ _____
1 candy _____
1 licorice rope _____
1 drink _____
Total $2.35

5. 1 drink _____
1 _____ _____
1 ice cream _____
Total $3.45

6. 4 _____ _____
1 drink _____
Total $8.90

7. 1 _____ _____
1 hot dog _____
1 ice cream _____
Total $2.45

8. 2 hot chocolates _____
2 _____ _____
Total $2.80

9. 1 coffee _____
1 hot chocolate _____
2 _____ _____
Total $2.85

10. 1 popcorn _____
1 _____ _____
1 hot pretzel _____
Total $2.15

11. 2 licorice ropes _____
2 popcorn _____
2 _____ _____
Total $3.60

12. 4 _____ _____
4 drinks _____
Total $7.60

Name _____

27 *Basic Skills/Problem Solving 4-5*

HORSING AROUND

Lucy E. Quine loves horses. She has saved $300 from her job at the stables, and she's thrilled to find a sale at the tack shop. Pay attention to the prices to help her get some good deals on riding clothes and equipment!

HALTER $30.00 20.00

BRIDLE $59.00 43.25

LEAD ROPE $15.00 11.50

BIT $25.00 18.80

SADDLE $300.00 250.10

BLANKET $65.00 44.50

CURRY BRUSH $10.00 $5.25

GIRTH $39.00 27.60

HELMET $75.00 55.90

BREECHES $80.00 39.90

DRESS BOOTS $110.00 $75.00

1. Could she afford to buy a horse blanket, boots, and a bridle?

_____

2. If she buys the saddle, how much will be left for other items?

_____

3. What three articles are each close to $40?

_____

_____

4. How much would she pay for the boots, helmet, and breeches?

_____

5. How much less is a halter than a bridle?

_____

6. How many lead ropes can she get for $30?

_____

7. What will it cost if she buys the most expensive item and the least expensive item together?

_____

8. Which item is about $50 less than the helmet?

_____

9. Will she pay more for a curry brush, blanket, and bit or a bridle and helmet?

_____

10. Choose the articles you would buy if you had $300 to spend. Don't go over $300!

_____

_____

_____

Name _____

WHERE'S THE FOOD?

After the volleyball tournament, the team is hungry. The girls have all ordered the food they want, but they're wondering what's taking so long! Meanwhile, the coach is wondering just how much this is all going to cost. Find the total cost for each player.

EAT AT THE
MENU TREE

Tacos	80¢
Burritos	99¢
Hot Dogs	$1.50
Hamburgers	$1.75
Pizza Slice	$1.25
Sandwiches	$1.90
Rice Bowl	$1.00
Fries	95¢
Salad	$1.10
Chips	50¢
Shakes	$1.50
Drinks	99¢
Ice Cream	95¢
Candy	45¢

Annie Ace
salad
burrito
choc. shake
2 tacos
TOTAL

Movin' Marika
fries
hamburger
3 candy bars
van. shake
TOTAL

Daring Donna
fries
salad
sandwich
choc. shake
TOTAL

Suzie Spiker
2 pizzas
drink
chips
ice cream
TOTAL

Jumpin' Julie
2 fries
3 hot dogs
choc. shake
pizza
TOTAL

Colleen Cool
salad
rice bowl
pizza
drink
TOTAL

Towering Tara
pizza
salad
hamburger
drink
ice cream
TOTAL

No-Foul Fran
hot dog
3 burritos
fries
van. shake
3 candy bars
TOTAL

Sally Smasher
salad
2 fries
van. shake
candy
TOTAL

Nellie Net
2 chips
rice bowl
taco
sandwich
TOTAL

Sara Server
3 hot dogs
pizza
choc. shake
taco
TOTAL

Power Pam
2 chips
2 tacos
3 candy bars
choc. shake
TOTAL

Name

BUMPS, BRUISES, & BREAKS

The Blue Berg Hockey Team never makes it through a game without some injuries. It looks as if Bruiser is out of the game for a while! Help the team solve some of their injury problems by deciding what operation is needed for each one. (Some may need more than one.) Write **A** (*add*), **S** (*subtract*), **M** (*multiply*), or **D** (*divide*) next to each problem. Then use a separate piece of paper to find the answers.

_____ **1.** The cost of hospital trips for the Blue Bergs averages $125,000 a season. If the season is five months long, what is the average monthly hospital cost for the season? _____

_____ **2.** The Blue Bergs had a total of 396 teeth intact when they started the season. They lost 45 of them. How many teeth did the team have left at the end of the season? _____

_____ **3.** Pierre, the goalie, lost an average of 27 minutes per game because of bloody noses. How many games did he play in if he lost 135 minutes total for his nosebleeds? _____

_____ **4.** Each defensive player bumped his shins and bruised his nose a total of 26 times in each game period. There are 3 game periods and 2 defensive players. At this rate, how many bumps and bruises will they get in the entire game? _____

_____ **5.** In one season, 12 of the 130 total injuries were broken bones and torn ligaments, 53 were broken or lost teeth, and 30 were black eyes. The rest were bumps and bruises. How many were bumps and bruises? _____

_____ **6.** Two team members got food poisoning the morning of the big game. Twice that many had colds and couldn't play. Three more were on crutches. If there are 18 players on the team, how many were left to play the game? _____

_____ **7.** During one game, a referee called minor penalties on Big Bruno and Biffo for roughing. Five more players got minor penalties for tripping and 3 more for high sticking. If a minor penalty is 2 minutes in the penalty box, how many total minutes did the team spend in the penalty box during the game? _____

_____ **8.** In one game alone, there were these injuries: one player had a hockey stick broken over his head, two guys got in a bloody fist fight, and five more got cut by skates to the cheek. All of them had to take time out from the game. How many players got called off the ice for injuries? _____

Name

UP & OVER

Horses can leap over the most troublesome obstacles. Don't let these obstacles stop the horse from a great race. Fill in the correct signs on each jump to get the answer shown. Write + or – or x or ÷ in each of the blanks. (The first one is done for you!)

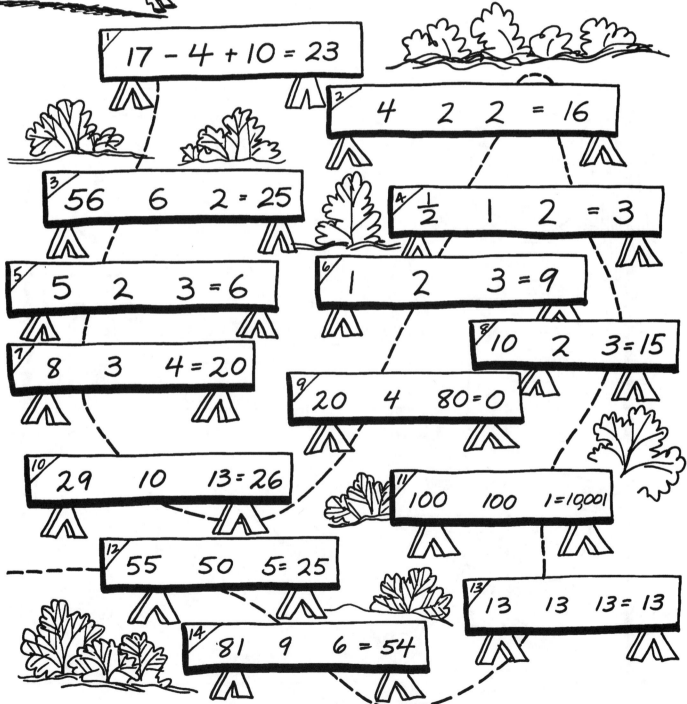

1. $17 - 4 + 10 = 23$

2. $4 \quad 2 \quad 2 = 16$

3. $56 \quad 6 \quad 2 = 25$

4. $\frac{1}{2} \quad 1 \quad 2 = 3$

5. $5 \quad 2 \quad 3 = 6$

6. $1 \quad 2 \quad 3 = 9$

7. $8 \quad 3 \quad 4 = 20$

8. $10 \quad 2 \quad 3 = 15$

9. $20 \quad 4 \quad 80 = 0$

10. $29 \quad 10 \quad 13 = 26$

11. $100 \quad 100 \quad 1 = 10{,}001$

12. $55 \quad 50 \quad 5 = 25$

13. $13 \quad 13 \quad 13 = 13$

14. $81 \quad 9 \quad 6 = 54$

Name

BEACH BAG JUMBLE

When Megan returned from her swimming workout in the ocean, she dumped her beach bag on the blanket and settled down for a snack. Find the perimeter (**P**), area (**A**), or volume (**V**) for each of the items that were in her bag. Choose the right formula to find each answer.

Perimeter = sum of all sides
Area of triangle = $\frac{1}{2}$b x h
Area of circle = π x r²
Volume of cylinder = π x r² x h

Circumference of circle = π x d
Area of rectangle = l x w
Volume of cube = s x s x s
Volume of rectangular prism = l x w x h

Name

DIAMONDS, RINGS, & COURTS

Athletes do plenty of running around, swimming, shooting across, or working with big surfaces. What area is covered by their sport? Choose the right formula from the center to find the area of each sports surface shown in the pictures. Write each answer in square units on the line.

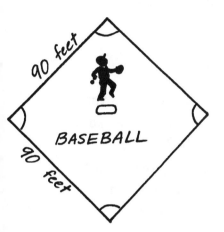

90 feet

90 feet

BASEBALL

1. Area = _____

TENNIS

36 feet

78 feet

2. Area = _____

BOXING

16 feet

16 feet

3. Area = _____

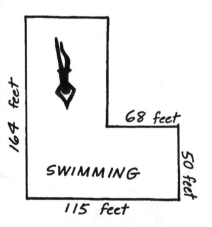

164 feet

68 feet

50 feet

SWIMMING

115 feet

4. Area = _____

FORMULAS FOR AREA

square $A = s \times s$

rectangle $A = l \times w$

circle $A = \pi \times r^2$

triangle $A = \frac{1}{2} b \times h$

trapezoid $A = h \times \frac{(b_1 + b_2)}{2}$

ARCHERY

75 feet

15 feet

5. Area = _____

WRESTLING

12 feet

6. Area = _____

TRACK

200 feet

600 feet

7. Area = _____

18 feet

3 feet

12 feet

SAILING

8 feet

8. Area = _____

Name _____

Basic Skills/Problem Solving 4-5

HANG TEN PERCENT

The surf's up at Shark Beach! One hundred surfers showed up on Saturday to "hang ten" for the awesome waves. If a surfer is "hanging ten percent"—what would that mean? See if you can figure it out!

Choose the correct percentage from the waves below to match the fraction in each problem. Write the answer on the line. Some answers may be used more than once.

Remember: To write a fraction as a percent, you have to write an equivalent fraction with a denominator of 100. For example: $\frac{1}{5} = \frac{20}{100} = 20\%$!

____% 1. $\frac{3}{4}$ of the surfers fell off their boards.

____% 2. $\frac{1}{10}$ can hang ten.

____% 3. $\frac{1}{5}$ forgot their sunscreen.

____% 4. $\frac{9}{10}$ are afraid of sharks.

____% 5. $\frac{1}{4}$ wear sunglasses at all times.

____% 6. $\frac{8}{10}$ wax their own boards.

____% 7. $\frac{1}{2}$ have been stung by jellyfish.

____% 8. $\frac{4}{10}$ have sand in their swimsuits.

____% 9. $\frac{1}{20}$ have never seen a shark.

____% 10. $\frac{6}{20}$ saw a shark today.

____% 11. $\frac{55}{100}$ have had surfing injuries.

____% 12. $\frac{3}{20}$ are very sunburned.

____% 13. $\frac{27}{30}$ learned to surf very young.

____% 14. $\frac{9}{12}$ forgot to eat breakfast.

____% 15. $\frac{10}{100}$ are over 50 years old.

____% 16. $\frac{4}{16}$ did not fall today.

____% 17. $\frac{3}{10}$ never had a surfing lesson.

____% 18. $\frac{2}{5}$ got smashed by the last wave.

____% 19. $\frac{4}{5}$ are high school students.

____% 20. $\frac{11}{22}$ have on wet suits today.

90%   75%   50%   25%   15%   80%   5%   10%   30%   20%   55%   40%

Name _____

"BUT COACH, CAN WE REST NOW?"

What are the coaches cooking up now? They are probably trying to figure out ways to keep their players working, improving, and winning. Here are some of the statistics the coaches must consider. Help them use percentages to find the numbers they need.

To find 30% of 80, move the decimal 2 places to the left and multiply: 0.30 x 80 = 240.0 or 240.

Find the number that represents each percentage.

_____ 1. Of the 20 players on Coach Jammin's team, 40% can dunk.

_____ 2. Rob swam 60% of the 120 laps that Coach Samantha Swimm asked for him to do.

_____ 3. Coach Strikeout ordered 20 new ball caps for his team. Only 5% arrived on time.

_____ 4. There were 360 runners at Coach Swift's home meet, but only 15% ran the hurdles.

_____ 5. Coach Wrencher's wrestlers won 75% of their 24 matches.

_____ 6. Only 10% of the 30 wrestlers want Coach Wrencher's bulldog Daisy to be the team mascot.

_____ 7. Coach P. J. Puck's hockey team traveled 1,200 miles last year, and 80% of the travel was on the team bus.

_____ 8. Coach Vicki Volley was not happy when 80% of the 30 players threw their towels on the locker room floor.

_____ 9. When Coach George T. Down invited his 80 football players to dinner, 90% of them ate the pizza he served.

_____ 10. By the end of the season, 15% of Coach Marcy Mogul's 60 skiers were injured.

Name _____

TIME OUT

The Cramville basketball team is crammed into their bus for the big game. It is a long ride to Eagleton, and the Cramville Comets are having some unexpected stops along the way. Solve these problems about their trip.

_____ 1. The team left Cramville at 8:00 A.M. They stopped for gas at 9:05 A.M. How long were they on the road before stopping?

_____ 2. They got stuck in the mud at the gas station, so their gas stop ended up being 45 minutes. What time did they get underway again?

_____ 3. Oops! A flat tire at 10:50 A.M. took them 20 minutes to change. What time was it when they got back on the road?

_____ 4. Just 90 minutes later, they hit a terrible snowstorm that stopped them for another hour. What time did they start moving again?

_____ 5. The van stopped for a snack and restroom break at 2:55 P.M. They headed toward Eagleton again at 3:15 P.M. How long was their stop?

_____ 6. An accident backed up traffic for miles. They stopped at 4:10 P.M. and didn't move again for 55 minutes. What time was it when they got moving again?

_____ 7. At 5:50 P.M., they were held up again! This time a fierce windstorm had knocked trees down across the road. The road was cleared at 6:20 P.M. How long did they wait?

_____ 8. Everyone was starved for dinner. Their hour-long dinner stop ended at 8:35 P.M. When did they stop for dinner?

_____ 9. Two hours and twenty minutes after their dinner stop ended, the Comets finally arrived at their motel in Eagleton. What time did they arrive?

_____ 10. The trip was expected to take 6 hours. How much longer than that did it take?

Name

RACK UP THE SAVINGS

When athletes shop for sports clothing, they need to have some good math skills to figure out their costs. Taxes add to the cost of the clothing. Discounts lower the prices. Solve these problems for the shoppers. (Round prices to the nearest penny.)

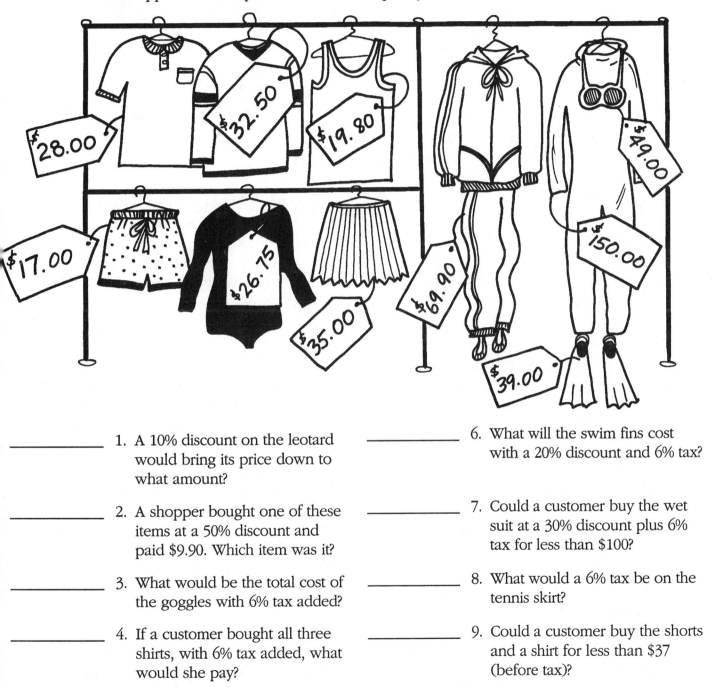

_____ 1. A 10% discount on the leotard would bring its price down to what amount?

_____ 2. A shopper bought one of these items at a 50% discount and paid $9.90. Which item was it?

_____ 3. What would be the total cost of the goggles with 6% tax added?

_____ 4. If a customer bought all three shirts, with 6% tax added, what would she pay?

_____ 5. What would a customer pay for the warm-up suit with a 25% discount (before tax)?

_____ 6. What will the swim fins cost with a 20% discount and 6% tax?

_____ 7. Could a customer buy the wet suit at a 30% discount plus 6% tax for less than $100?

_____ 8. What would a 6% tax be on the tennis skirt?

_____ 9. Could a customer buy the shorts and a shirt for less than $37 (before tax)?

_____ 10. What would be the cost of the warm-up suit with a 35% discount and 6% tax?

Name _____

CHILL OUT

Athletes drink lots of refreshing drinks, use plenty of towels, and get many uniforms dirty. You won't need to know an exact answer for these problems about their drinks, towels, and uniforms. Sometimes a close answer is just fine! Practice your estimation skills by circling the closest answer.

1. Each kid on the track team drinks about $2\frac{1}{2}$ gallons of water at each meet. There are 12 on the team. How much water do they drink each meet?

   10 gal   50 gal   30 gal   24 gal

2. There are eight tug-of-war teams with 10 or 11 on each team. They each use 2 towels apiece. About how many towels will they use?

   11   110   160   800

3. Each drinking cup at the snack shack gets filled with about $\frac{1}{4}$ cup of ice. On Sunday, 20 cups of ice were used. How many drinking cups were used?

   4   80   120   40

4. After the game, half of the football team uses 2 sticks of deodorant each. The other half uses 1 stick each. There are usually about 25 team members at a game. How much deodorant do they need?

   40 sticks   400 sticks
   4,000 sticks   100 sticks

5. A 5-gallon jug of SLAM Sports Drink serves about 30 thirsty kids. If 92 kids show up at Field Day, how many jugs will be needed?

   30   50   3   300

6. Three kids on the relay team made T-shirts to replace the worn-out shirts for their team. They bought the shirts for $3 and sold them for $5.95. If they bought 30 shirts and sold them all, about how much money did they make?

   $900 $190 $90 $180

7. The coach found 3 lockers full of smelly socks at the end of the season. He counted 23 pairs in one locker. If the others had about the same, how many pairs would he need to wash?

   75 pairs   50 pairs
   90 pairs   150 pairs

8. If seven runners each wear out about four pairs of $90 shoes a year, how much will they spend on shoes (total of all 4)?

   $2,800 $560 $360 $800

9. Mothers of the soccer players wash the uniforms 3 times a week. How many washings will take place for 22 players over a 10-week season?

   220   66   660   6,600

Name

FANTASTIC FINISHES

Who finished first? Pictures, diagrams, or models can help you figure out which runner is the winner in problem #1. For problems 2–5, draw a picture or diagram to help you figure out who finished first in each of these races.

1. Toby crossed the finish line ahead of Tony but behind Timothy. Terence and Tiny finished ahead of Timothy. Tiny was 3 places ahead of Toby. Label the runners in the picture.

2. In a softball throwing competition, the Frequent Fliers threw farther than the Airborne Aces, but not as far as the Iron Arms. The Speed Demons threw farther than the Airborne Aces, but not as far as the Frequent Fliers. Who won first place?

4. Skateboarder Sam finished his race ahead of Sara who finished behind Suzie and Stuart. Serena finished 4 places ahead of Sara. Who finished first?

3. In the volleyball tournament, the Pacers won more games than the Panthers but fewer than the Grizzlies. The Panthers won more games than the Giants. Who came in first?

5. Runner Thomas finished ahead of James and behind Ramon. Andrew finished behind James. Michael came in ahead of Andrew but behind James. Who came in first?

Name

CRISS-CROSS BIKE RACE

In this bicycle race, each cyclist will follow a different path. The four paths will cross each other many times. Start with biker #1. Using mental math, do the operation on the first flag. (Add 7 and 1.) Draw a path to the circle that has that answer. Then take that answer and do the operation shown on its flag. Draw the path to the next circle. Keep drawing the path until the cyclist arrives at a trophy.

Go back and draw the paths for the other three cyclists the same way. Use a different color to draw each path. Always pay attention to what the flags tell you to do with the numbers!

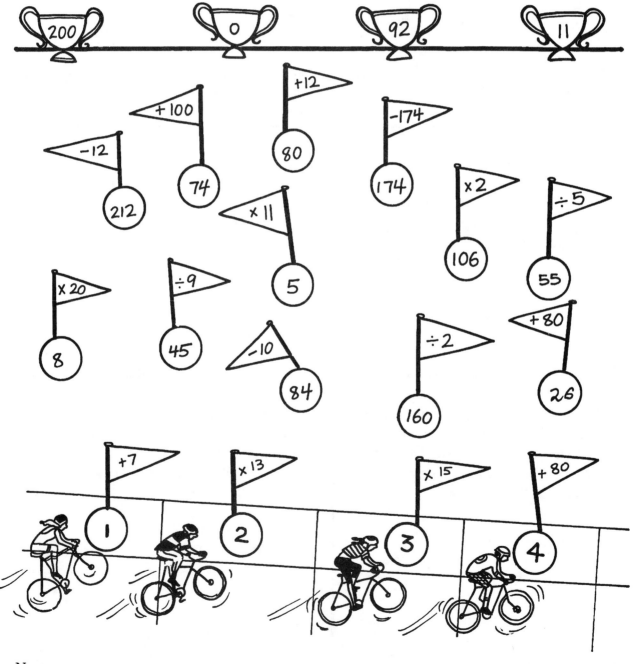

Name

HITTING THE BRICKS

If you're going to learn to break bricks with your head, you will have to practice a few times (or more) before you get it right! Sometimes you might not get it quite right. **Trial and Error** is one strategy for problem solving. Here's how it works: You choose an answer you think might work and try it out. If it doesn't fit, keep trying until you find one that works!

Lee is getting ready for a karate demonstration at his dojo next week. Each day he breaks a different number of bricks to get ready. By thinking about the clues, find the number he breaks each day.

SUNDAY
An even 2-digit number
Larger than 6 but smaller than 12
_____

MONDAY
Multiple of 40
Greater than 100
Less than 600
No digits of 1, 2, 3, 6, or 8
Only one 0
_____

TUESDAY
A 2-digit multiple of 7
Less than 50
Greater than 20
An even number
No digits over 5
_____

WEDNESDAY
An even 2-digit number
Multiple of 3
Digits add up to 6
Over 16
Less than 30
_____

THURSDAY
An odd number less than 99
Two digits
Divisible by 25
_____

FRIDAY
An even 2-digit number
Even number between 50 and 150
Digits total 1
_____

SATURDAY
An even number between 50 and 70
Digits total 11
Digits are in order (small to large)
_____

Name _____

41 *Basic Skills/Problem Solving 4-5*

LOCKER ROOM LOGIC

Coach Crunch has been looking all day for the tennis player who left a Gorgonzola cheese in her locker. It's leaking out and getting pretty stinky. Whose locker is this? The players whose lockers are in this area are Chrissy, Cathy, Carla, Camille, and Cass. Use the clues and logical thinking to figure out who is the owner of the stinky locker.

1. Cass's locker is next to Camille's.

2. Camille's locker is #20.

3. The cheese is not in Cathy's locker.

4. Carla's locker number is 10 less than Chrissy's.

5. Cathy's locker is next to Chrissy's.

The cheese is in _____'s locker.

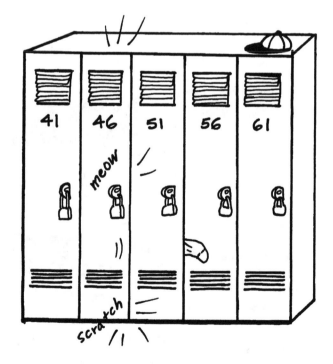

Just after the coach got the cheese problem settled, Max, the cat, decided to take a nap on someone's sweaty socks. The coach needs your help again to find the owner of Locker #46. The locker list shows these names: Randy, Reed, R.J., Rick, and Ray.

1. Ray's and Randy's lockers are not together.

2. Randy's locker is on one end.

3. Reed's locker has the highest number.

4. Rich's locker is next to Reed's.

Max is awake and trying to get out of _____'s locker.

Name

42

LOGICAL LINEUP

Finally, the Bigtown Bears are in the playoffs. The ticket line has been growing since early morning. Solve the problems about the lineup by looking at the pictures and using logical thinking.

**Problem 1: Jamie forgot the money, but hasn't discovered it yet.
Figure out which one is Jamie. Circle Jamie.**

1. Jamie is in front of a person with curly hair.

2. Jess is in front of Jamie, but behind Moe.

3. Moe is first in line.

4. Lee is last in line.

5. There are two people between Jamie and Moe.

**Problem 2: Two of these fans will get seats in the front row. Put
a box around each of them.**

1. Neither of them is first in line.

2. Neither wears glasses.

3. One of them is in the last half of the line.

4. Neither of them is a Bear's fan.

Name _____

GRIDIRON SOLUTIONS

A gridiron is another name for a football field. The aim of a football game is to score more points than the other team by crossing the opponent's goal line with the ball. Points are scored in many ways. The chart under the goalpost below shows the ways to score points. Notice that extra points with kicks, runs, or passes can only occur after a touchdown!

If the Grizzlies scored 30 points in a game, they might have collected these points in a few different ways. Here are a few:

$$5 \text{ TD} = 30 \text{ points}$$
$$10 \text{ FG} = 30 \text{ points}$$
$$3 \text{ TD} + 3 \text{ XK} + 3 \text{ FG} = 30 \text{ points}$$

$$4 \text{ TD} + 3 \text{ XK} + 1 \text{ FG} = 30 \text{ points}$$
$$3 \text{ FG} + 3 \text{ TD} + 1 \text{ XRP} + 1 \text{ XK} = 30 \text{ points}$$
$$1 \text{ S} + 3 \text{ TD} + 2 \text{ XRP} + 2 \text{ FG} = 30 \text{ points}$$

TD = touchdown = 6 points

XK = (kick) extra point after touchdown = 1 point

XRP = (run or pass) extra point after touchdown = 2 points

FG = field goal = 3 points

S = safety = 2 points

Write 3 or more equations to show how the Grizzlies might have scored their points in each game described.

1. The first game of the season ended with a 16 to 16 tie.

_____

_____

_____

2. The Grizzlies won the second game 49 to 18.

_____

_____

_____

Use with page 45.

Name

44

GRIDIRON SOLUTIONS, cont.

Write 3 or more different equations to show how the Grizzlies might have scored their points in each game described.

3. In the game against the Cougars, the toughest game of the season, the Grizzlies scored 37 points.

_____

_____

_____

4. Oh, oh! The only loss of the season came to the Vikings. The Grizzlies lost in a close one: 21 to 20.

_____

_____

_____

5. The homecoming game was a great victory. The Grizzlies won 56 to 18.

_____

_____

_____

6. The final game of the season ended in another tie. The score was 29 to 29.

_____

_____

_____

Use with page 44.

Name _____

45   *Basic Skills/Problem Solving 4-5*

JUST HANGING AROUND

STRATEGIES
- Trial and Error
- Write an Equation
- Draw a Diagram
- Make a Chart
- Make a Graph
- Use Mental Math
- Use a Formula
- Estimate

Gymnasts hang around the gym a lot. They practice for hours and plan strategies for winning at their sport. For every one of these problems about gymnasts, choose the strategy that you think would best help you find the answer. Then use that strategy to solve the problem.

1. The rings are suspended 98 in. from the floor. Is this about 8 ft? _____

    a. draw a diagram
    b. use mental math
    c. write an equation

2. The gymnasts are lined up at the drinking fountain. Fred is 2 people behind Ned. Ned is 3 people in front of Ted. Ed is just behind Ned. Who is last in line?

    _____

    a. write an equation
    b. draw a diagram
    c. trial and error

3. There are 6 events in men's gymnastics. If the judges each score only 1 event, and each event has 5 judges, how many judges will there be? _____

    a. use mental math
    b. write an equation
    c. make a graph

4. The bleachers in the gym are 22 ft long. How many people can sit in a row if each person takes up about 2 ft of space?

    _____

    a. make a chart
    b. estimate
    c. use a formula

5. The coach added up the number of gymnasts he has coached in each of the last 6 years. The numbers were 13, 10, 20, 7, 8, and 8. What is the total number he has coached? _____

    a. use mental math
    b. make a chart
    c. make a graph

6. The mat on which Scott will do his floor routine is 12 meters by 12 meters. What is the area of the mat? _____

    a. trial and error
    b. use a formula
    c. write an equation

Name _____

46

PRACTICE MAKES PERFECT

Gymnasts practice for hours. These hours add up to weeks, months, and even years! Practice your problem-solving skills by choosing strategies to solve these problems about the gymnasts and their sport. Choose the strategy you think is best for each problem and find the answer if possible.

STRATEGIES
- Trial and Error
- Write an Equation
- Draw a Diagram
- Make a Chart
- Make a Graph
- Use Mental Math
- Use a Formula
- Estimate

1. Terry's balance beam routine includes a walkover into a somersault. The walkover takes about 5 feet to execute, and the somersault takes about twice that. Can she do both on the 16.5-foot beam?

   _____

2. The floor exercise area is a 40-foot square. If Terry's routine takes her across and back 6 complete times, how many feet will she travel?

   _____

3. At the State meet, the Flips earned 123 points. The Stars earned 63 less, while the Swoop won with three times what the Stars earned. What was the Swoop's score?

   _____

4. The High School meet started at 2:30 P.M. The 4 events each took $\frac{1}{2}$ hour with a ten-minute break after each and a $\frac{1}{2}$-hour awards ceremony at the end. What time was the meet over?

   _____

5. Lucy fell off the beam fewer times than Jana. Jana fell less than Terri but more than Pasha. Terri fell more than Raina, and Raina fell more than Jana. Pasha fell more than Lucy. Who fell the least of all?

   _____

6. Three gymnasts are each 6 years apart in ages. The total of their ages is 33. What are their ages?

   _____

Name _____

SUBMERGED SOLUTIONS

Often when you solve a problem, all that shows on paper is the answer. The way that you solved the problem is not shown. It is submerged in your mind, but no one else can see it. Sometimes, you don't even stop to think about what you **did** to solve the problem.

When you solve these underwater problems (on pages 48 and 49), pay attention to how you go about getting the answer. Solve each problem, write your answer, and then explain how you found the solution. You may draw diagrams or pictures as a part of your explanation.

1. A school of barracudas swam past Samantha. She saw twice as many lobsters as barracudas, and three more angelfish than lobsters. She saw 25 angelfish. How many barracudas did she see?

   _____

   How did you solve this problem?

   _____
   _____
   _____
   _____

2. Scuba diver Samantha got to the sunken ship before Seth, but not before Tabitha and Josiah. Dara got to the ship before Josiah, but after Tabitha. Who got to the ship last?

   _____

   How did you solve this problem?

   _____
   _____
   _____
   _____

Use with page 49.

Name

48

3. Josiah spent $280 on new scuba gear. Then he bought a new underwater camera for $112 and an underwater watch for $56. Since he made some money from the sale of his old gear, he only had to come up with $362 for the new gear. How much did he get from the sale of the old gear? _____

How did you solve this problem?

_____

_____

4. The divers fed the fish half of the food in a cube-shaped container. Each side of the cube measured 12 inches. If the container was full to start with, what is the volume of food given to the fish? _____

How did you solve this problem?

_____

_____

Challenge!

5. Tabitha and Dara have been diving a number of years that is half of the age of Dara. Dara is 3 years older than Tabitha. The total of their ages is 33.
   How old is Tabitha? _____ How old is Dara? _____

   How long have they been diving? _____

How did you solve this problem?

_____

_____

_____

_____

Use with page 48.

Name _____

49

HITTING THEIR STRIDE

Speed skaters need to get into a rhythm of the right stride in order to achieve their fastest possible time. See how accurate you can be in checking out the answers to these problems. If the answer to a problem is correct, color the matching section on the speed skating track.

1. Skating time of $\frac{3}{4}$ hour = 75 minutes

2. 3 races of 1500 m each = 4500 m

3. 2 feet = 0.2 of 10 feet

4. 200 m = 0.2 of 1000 m race

5. 14 hours = 140 minutes

6. $\frac{1}{2}$ of $\frac{1}{4}$ = $\frac{1}{4}$

7. 9% of 90 = 10

8. $\frac{1}{3}$ is equivalent to $\frac{3}{9}$.

9. The formula for a perimeter of a triangle is s + s + s.

10. $\frac{5}{50}$, 10%, $\frac{1}{10}$, and 0.1 all mean the same amount.

11. 9 minutes 1 second minus 2 minutes 50 seconds is 7 minutes 51 seconds

12. The difference between −14° and +74° is 60°

13. 40% = 0.4 = $\frac{4}{10}$ = $\frac{2}{5}$

14. 0.2 seconds x 0.4 seconds = 0.008 seconds

15. Eight speed skaters ate 1.5 lb of pasta each. This totals 12 lb of pasta.

16. One hundred times one thousand is one million.

Name

APPENDIX

Contents

PROBLEM-SOLVING STRATEGIES

USE A FORMULA

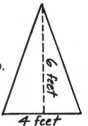

When you need to find a measurement (such as for perimeter, area, or volume), use a formula. Make sure you find the correct formula for the task you want to do.

The formula for the area of a triangle is $A = \frac{1}{2} b \times h$ ($\frac{1}{2} \times base \times height$).
The area of this triangle is $\frac{1}{2} \times 4\,ft \times 6\,ft = 12\,ft^2$.

ESTIMATE

Many times you can figure out a solution by doing an approximate calculation. This strategy works well when you do not need an exact answer.

There were 4,870 fans watching the hockey game. One-fifth of them ate a hot dog. About how many hot dogs were sold?

You can estimate that since 4,870 is close to 5,000, and $\frac{1}{5}$ of 5,000 is 1,000, then about 1,000 hot dogs were sold.

TRIAL AND ERROR

Sometimes, you just have to choose a reasonable answer and then see if it works! Keep trying until you find an answer that does work.

There is a number that has 3 digits, each larger than 4. The sum of the digits is 19. Two of the digits are the same, but they are not next to each other. The digit in the tens place is 4 more than the other digits.

(Keep trying until you find that the number is 595!)

MENTAL MATH

This is a very handy strategy. You just solve simple problems in your head! You don't even need a calculator or pencil and paper.

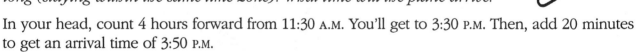

The bobsled team's plane left at 11:30 A.M., and the flight is 4 hours 20 minutes long (staying within the same time zone). What time will the plane arrive?

In your head, count 4 hours forward from 11:30 A.M. You'll get to 3:30 P.M. Then, add 20 minutes to get an arrival time of 3:50 P.M.

CHANGE INTO AN EQUATION

If a problem has several numbers mixed in with the words, it will be helpful to write the problem as a number sentence.

Tammi did 15 jumps in practice today. Sara did 4 more than Tammi, and Jenny did 4 less than Tammi. How many jumps did they do all together?

You can write this equation:

$$15 + (15 + 4) + (15 - 4) = n$$

You'll find that the skaters did a total of 45 jumps.

CHANGE ALL THE FACTS TO A COMMON FORM

When facts are written in different units, change each fact to a common unit before you do the operation to solve the problem.

James showered for 7 minutes 50 seconds. Juan showered for $\frac{1}{4}$ hour. Ari showered for 185 seconds. Sam showered for 6 minutes 15 seconds. What was the total time of all the showers?

Change all the facts to seconds and add.

(James) 470 sec + (Juan) 900 sec + (Ari) 185 sec + (Sam) 375 sec = 1930 sec (or 32 minutes 10 seconds)

DRAW A DIAGRAM

Some problems just need a picture! For a complicated problem, it often works well to draw a picture or diagram.

Chuck finished the race before Tom, but after Roy. Roy finished between Andrew and Brad. Tom was the fourth runner behind Andrew. Who won the race? (Answer: Andrew)

SIMPLIFY THE PROBLEM

Some problems can be made simpler by rewriting them into a shorter question.

How many falls did a snowboarder take if she fell on 22% of the 350 tricks she tried this week? The simple question is: What is 22% of 350?

MAKE A GRAPH OR CHART

When you have a lot of scores or other statistics that fall into different categories, it is helpful to draw a quick graph or chart. For instance, if you know how 5 different divers scored on 5 different dives in a competition, and you need to answer some questions about the scores, a chart can help you answer such questions as this:

Which diver had the highest total scores? Who had the lowest score? On which dives did three divers get the same score?

	1	2	3	4	5
Dave	9.0	9.7	6.1	8.7	10
Doug	7.4	9.5	10	8.3	7.7
Derek	8.6	9.4	8.5	7.9	9.6
Don	7.6	6.4	8.1	10	7.8
Dudley	8.9	9.2	9.6	8.4	9.1

DRAW A NUMBER LINE

If you are adding and/or subtracting a number of facts, a number line can be helpful. Make a number line that goes higher than the facts you have. Then draw arrows for each step of the problem.

After the kickoff, the Bears caught the ball at the 5 yard line. They rushed forward 25 yards. On the next down, they passed the ball forward for a gain of 20 yards. Then a penalty set them back 15 yards. On the next down, a long pass and run gained them 57 yards. Did they make a touchdown?

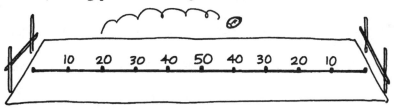

GLOSSARY

ACCURACY — The correctness of a problem solution.

AREA — The measure of the region inside a closed plane figure. Area is measured in square units.

AVERAGE — The sum of a set of numbers divided by the number of addends. *The average of 22 + 51 + 10 + 75 + 16 + 60 = $\frac{234}{6}$ = 39.*

DATA — A set of scores or information.

DECIMAL — A name for a numeral that is expressed with a decimal point. *0.06, 100.5, 3.017 are decimal numerals.*

DIAGRAM — A drawing used to illustrate a problem or a problem solution.

DIGIT — A symbol used to write numerals. *The decimal system's digits are 0, 1, 2, 3, 4, 5, 6, 7, 8, 9.*

DISCOUNT — A deduction made from the regular price of an item.

DIVISIBILITY — A number is divisible by another number if the quotient is a whole number with no remainder. *192 is divisible by 6 because 192 ÷ 6 = 32, a whole number.*

EQUATION — A mathematical sentence that says two parts are equal. *80 ÷ 8 + 4 = 14 and 1,000 ÷ 100 x 10 + 10 = 110 are equations.*

ESTIMATE — An approximate answer to a problem.

EVEN NUMBER — A number that is divisible by 2 with no remainder.

FACTOR — One of 2 or more numbers that can be multiplied to find a product. *6 x 8 = 48, so 6 and 8 are factors of 48. 1, 2, 3, 4, 12, 16, and 24 are also factors of 48.*

FORMULA — A rule or fact written in mathematical symbols and numbers.

FRACTION — A number that compares part of an object or set to the whole object or set. Fractions are expressed in terms of $\frac{a}{b}$, and *b* cannot be 0. *$\frac{1}{2}$ and $\frac{3}{4}$ are fractions.*

GRAPH — A drawing that shows the relationships between sets of numbers.

LOGIC — A way of solving problems that uses principles of reasoning.

MENTAL MATH — Solving problems in your head without using any tools.

METRIC MEASUREMENTS — A system of measurements based on the decimal system.

MIXED NUMERAL — A numeral that mixes a whole number with a fractional numeral or a decimal numeral.
$55\frac{1}{4}$ and 644.092 are mixed numerals.

MULTIPLE — The product of a whole number and any other whole number.
20 is a multiple of 5 because 4 x 5 = 20.

MULTISTEP PROBLEM — A problem that requires more than one operation, process, or step in finding a solution.

ODD NUMBER — A number that is not divisible by 2.
3, 13, 77, and 29 are odd numbers.

OPEN-ENDED PROBLEM — A problem that has more than one solution.

OPERATIONS — Processes that are performed on numbers.
Addition, subtraction, multiplication, and division are operations.

PERCENT — A comparison of a number with 100.
25 is 25% of 100.

PERIMETER — Measurement of the distance around the outside of a figure.

PROBLEM-SOLVING STRATEGY — A method of finding the solution to a problem.

RATIO — A comparison between two numbers expressed as a fraction.
$\frac{a}{b}$, meaning $a \div b$.

SOLUTION — The answer to a problem.

STATISTICS — Numerical facts or data.

TAXES — A percentage of the cost of an item that is added to the price. The tax portion of a sale is usually collected by a government such as county, city, or state.

TRIAL AND ERROR — A problem-solving strategy that involves trying out different solutions until the correct one is found.

VOLUME — The measure of capacity or of space enclosed by a three-dimensional figure.

PROBLEM SOLVING
SKILLS TEST

100 possible points. Questions 1–70 are worth 1 point each.
Questions 71–74 are worth 5 points each. Question 75 is worth 10 points.

Solve these equations to find out what n is.

n = _____ 1. $60 - n + 80 = 100$ n = _____ 3. $25 \times n + 7 = 57$ n = _____ 5. $77.77 - 0.77 = n$

n = _____ 2. $4{,}000 \div n = 100$ n = _____ 4. $n = \frac{1}{2} + \frac{1}{4}$

Use the chart to answer questions 6–9.
Write the answers on the lines.

REFRESHING DRINKS	
Fresh Ade	$1.00
Thirst Quencher	$2.00
Gallon O' Gulp	$4.50
Squelch	$ .75
Big Swallow	$1.75
Ener-G	$2.50
Drench	$1.25
Lemon Drench	$2.50
Re-Vive	$3.00
Orange Dunk	$2.10

_____ 6. Which 2 drinks together would cost $7.50?

_____ 7. Could an athlete buy 2 Lemon Drenches and 2 Squelches for $5.00?

_____ 8. What would it cost to buy 2 Ener-Gs and 1 Big Swallow?

_____ 9. What drink costs $0.85 less than an Orange Dunk?

Write the letter of the equation that can be used to solve the problem.

_____ 10. Seven soccer players each scored 3 goals in the first game. Two players scored 2 goals in the second game and one player scored 4 in the third game. How many goals were scored?
a. $(7 + 3) + (2 + 1) + 4 = n$ b. $(7 \times 3) + (2 \times 2) + 4 = n$ c. $7 + 3 + 2 + 2 + 1 + 4 = n$

_____ 11. What is the answer to problem #10?

_____ 12. The Grizzlies spent $500 on travel and $350 on food and lodging on their trip to the state championship. Their fund started out with $1,000. How much money was left after the trip?
a. $\$500 - \$350 + \$1{,}000 = n$ b. $\$500 \times \$350 \times \$1{,}000 = n$
c. $\$1{,}000 + \$500 + \$350 = n$ d. $\$1{,}000 - \$500 - \$350 = n$

_____ 13. What is the answer to problem #12?

_____ 14. After the game, the swim team ate 4.4 giant pizzas. This was twice as many as they ate after the first game. How many did they eat all together after the 2 games?
a. $4.4 + (\frac{1}{2} \times 4.4) = n$ b. $4.4 + 2 \times 4.4 = n$
c. $2 \times (4.4 + \frac{1}{2}) = n$ d. $4.4 + 4.4 = n$

_____ 15. What is the answer to problem #14?

_____ 16. Write the letters of the information that is needed to solve the following problem. How many goal attempts by the Comets did the Black Hawk goalie stop?
a. The Comets attempted 49 goals.   b. The Black Hawks attempted 53 goals.
c. The Comets scored 3 goals.   d. The Black Hawks scored 5 goals.

Name _____

_____ 17. Write the letter or letters of the information NOT needed to solve the problem.
How many fans bought tickets to the homecoming game?
- a. The tickets sold brought in $26,664.
- b. There are seats for 4,850 people.
- c. 175 people stood to watch the game.
- d. The tickets cost $6.00 a piece.

18. Write a phrase telling what missing information is needed to solve the following problem.
The high school track team had 32 injuries last season. The football team had 7 injuries more than the tennis team. The ski team had 120 injuries. How many more injuries did the ski team have than the football, tennis, and track teams all together?
Missing information:

_____

Use the chart to answer questions 19–22.

_____ 19. Who has over 10 more bumps and bruises than Sy?

_____ 20. Who has $\frac{1}{3}$ of the bumps and bruises of Sal?

_____ 21. Who has 7 less than Sis?

_____ 22. Who has $\frac{1}{2}$ as many as Sal?

Write an equation to solve each problem.

23. Five snowboarders each spent $850.00 on their equipment. How much did they spend all together? _____

24. Twenty mountain climbers started for the summit. Nine stopped from sickness and one from an injury. Three of the sick climbers recovered and started climbing again. Four more climbers quit due to sunburn. How many got to the top? _____

25. On a very hot day, the ballpark collected $15,750 from drink sales. There were 7,500 drinks sold. How much did each drink cost? _____

Choose the correct operations for the problems. Write +, −, x, or ÷ in each space.

26. 16 ___ 8 ___ 5 = 10

28. 950 ___ 900 ___ 17 = 67

30. 5,000 ___ 2 ___ 5,002 = 0

27. 1,000 ___ 10 = 100

29. 80 ___ 80 ___ 80 = 80

Use the table to answer questions 31–34.

_____ 31. Which year was a bad one for Matt?

_____ 32. Who had the best years from 1995 through 1997?

_____ 33. Whose worst year had $\frac{1}{3}$ of the wins of his or her best year?

_____ 34. Whose best year had 6 wins less than Max's best year?

WINNING MATCHES

Player	1993	1994	1995	1996	1997	Totals
MAX	24	17	14	18	16	89
MATT	18	2	7	12	21	60
MOE	3	8	14	17	21	63
MUSA	7	18	10	15	21	71
MELODY	18	14	13	16	15	76
TOTALS	70	69	58	79	94	359

Name _____

57 *Basic Skills/Problem Solving 4-5*

Write the perimeter of each figure.

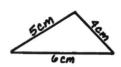

35. _____ 36. _____ 37. _____

Use mental math to find the answers for 38 and 39.

_____ 38. Each volleyball player uses 2 towels after each game, and they play 3 games a week. How many towels will be used in a week if the team has 20 players?

_____ 39. After each wrestling match, the wrestlers drink 0.8 gallons of water each. How much water will 100 wrestlers drink after two matches?

Write the area of each figure.

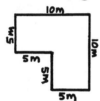

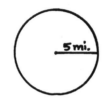

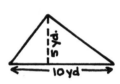

40. _____ 41. _____ 42. _____

Use the picture and prices below to answer questions 43–45.

_____ 43. Which would cost more: A and B together or C and D together?

_____ 44. How much more are the basketball shoes (A) than the soccer shoes (B)?

_____ 45. How much less are the boxing shoes (C) than the skates (D)?

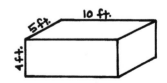

_____ 46. A basketball player shot 40 times for a basket, and 15 shots did not go in. Write a ratio that shows how many of the baskets shot did not score.

_____ 47. To get to the golf tournament, 35 players rode the bus, and 15 players drove themselves. Write a ratio that shows how many of the total players did not ride the bus.

Write the volume of each figure.

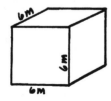

48. _____   49. _____

Name _____

Choose the letter of the percentage that shows each of these amounts.

a. 50% c. 60% e. 80%

b. 30% d. 40%

_____ 50. The team won 40 out of 50 games.

_____ 51. Su Lin had perfect scores on 3 of his 5 dives.

_____ 52. Koki knocked over 12 of the 24 hurdles he jumped.

Choose the letter of the fraction that shows each of these amounts.

a. $\frac{2}{5}$ c. $\frac{1}{10}$ e. $\frac{1}{4}$

b. $\frac{3}{5}$ d. $\frac{1}{5}$ f. $\frac{4}{5}$

_____ 53. 60% of the tickets are sold.

_____ 54. Team A ate 20% of the pizza.

_____ 55. Georgia won 25% of her tennis matches.

Use the picture and prices below to answer questions 56–60.

_____ 56. What would 5% tax on item D be?

_____ 57. On which item would a 5% tax come to $7.00?

_____ 58. With a 10% discount, what would item C cost?

_____ 59. Which item would cost about $19.00 with a 50% discount?

_____ 60. On which item would a 5% tax come to $4.50?

$37.95 $140.00 $15.00   E   B   D   A $90.00   C $26.80

Estimate the answers to problems 61 and 62 below.

_____ 61. For training, 31 swimmers each swim 8.5 miles a day. About how much distance is this all together?

_____ 62. A group of skiers stopped for hot chocolate. Eighteen skiers drank the good stuff, which cost $1.90 for a cup. One skier paid for all the drinks with a $50 bill. About how much change did she get back?

Give the solution to these problems about time.

_____ 63. The cross-country skiers left the starting gate at 7:30 A.M. The last skier crossed the finish line 6 hours 15 minutes later. At what time did the race end?

_____ 64. The golf team van arrived at the golf course in San Diego at 6:20 P.M. They had been traveling for 9 hours 20 minutes. They did not change time zones. What time did they leave home?

For questions 65 and 66, write the letter of the strategy that is best for solving the problem.

_____ 65. A bowler knocked down an average of 7 pins in each frame. She bowled 30 frames a day for 20 days. How many pins did she knock down in the 20 days?

    a. make a number line   c. write an equation

    b. estimate   d. draw a diagram

_____ 66. The swimmers lined up in order of their height. Jana was shorter than Tad who was taller than Michael and Anya. Anya was not next to Tad.

    a. make a graph   c. trial and error

    b. write a ratio   d. draw a diagram

For each problem 67–70, write YES or NO to tell if the answer is accurate.

_____ 67. The springs on Natasha's trampoline cost $2.50 each. How much would it cost to replace all 90? *Answer: $185.00.*

Name

_____ 68. Tasha's scuba diving equipment weighs $\frac{1}{20}$ of her body weight. Her equipment weighs 6 pounds. How much does Tasha weigh? *Answer: 120 pounds.*

_____ 69. Jamin did 32 pushups on Friday, 25 on Saturday, 40 on Sunday, and 13 on Tuesday. He did a total of 130 on the five days from Friday to Tuesday. How many did he do on Monday? *Answer: 20 pushups.*

_____ 70. Abby runs 4.5 miles a day. She has run 360.5 miles so far this year. How many days has she run? *Answer: 85 days.*

71. Use the illustration and logic to solve the following problem. Write the letter for the solution on the line.
The four bowlers had these scores today: 210, 250, 280, and 300.
The bowler with a 210 score has his bag packed already.
A bowler with earrings bowled a score of 280.
The bowler with shorts scored less than two other bowlers.
Which bowler had the perfect 300 score? _____

Write 2 different solutions for the problem below. Write the solutions on lines 72 and 73.
How many times did the sky diving team members jump today? The answer is a 2-digit odd number under 40. Both digits are odd. The sum of the digits is 10, and their product is odd.

72. Solution #1 _____

73. Solution #2 _____

74. Use the illustration and logic to solve this problem. Write the letter for the solution on the line.
The four fencers are named Ray, Chen, Li, and Stu.
Stu is on the right end.
Ray is between Li and Chen.
Stu is not next to Chen.
Which one is Chen? _____

75. Find the solution for this problem. Then tell how you solved it. You may use drawings, diagrams, or equations in your explanation.
Georgia is a great golfer, but today has been a bad day. She has lost a lot of balls. While searching in the woods for the golf balls, she found 24 coins totaling $2.40. The coins were not all dimes. What were the coins? Answer: _____

How I solved this: _____

_____

_____

_____

Name _____

ANSWER KEY

Skills Test

1. 40
2. 40
3. 2
4. $\frac{3}{4}$
5. 77
6. Gallon O'Gulp & Re-Vive
7. no
8. $6.75
9. Drench
10. b
11. 29
12. d
13. $150
14. a
15. 6.6
16. a, c
17. b, c
18. number of injuries on the tennis team
19. Sam
20. Sly
21. Sue
22. Sara
23. 5 x $850.00 = n
24. 20 − 9 − 1 + 3 − 4 = n
25. $15,750 ÷ 7,500 = n
26. 16 ÷ 8 x 5 = 10
27. 1,000 ÷ 10 = 100
28. 950 − 900 + 17 = 67
29. 80 + 80 − 80 = 80
30. 5,000 + 2 − 5,002 = 0
31. 1994
32. Moe
33. Musa
34. Melody
35. 31.4 cm
36. 15 cm
37. 80 cm
38. 120
39. 160 gal
40. 75 m²
41. 78.5 mi²
42. 25 yd²
43. C & D
44. $19.50
45. $144.05
46. $\frac{15}{40}$ or $\frac{3}{8}$
47. $\frac{15}{50}$ or $\frac{3}{10}$
48. 216 m³
49. 200 ft³
50. e
51. c
52. a
53. b
54. d
55. e
56. $0.75
57. E
58. $24.12
59. B
60. A
61. 270 or 300 mi
62. $10.00
63. 1:45 P.M.
64. 9:00 A.M.
65. c
66. d
67. no
68. yes
69. yes
70. no
71. D
72–73. Solutions are 37 and 19.
74. A
75. Solutions will vary. Check to see that solution is correct. (One solution is 20 dimes, 1 quarter, and 3 nickels.) Give student points depending on solution accuracy and completeness of solution explanation.

Skills Exercises

pages 10–11

1. a, c, 50 cups
2. c, d, 64.4 meters
3. a, c, 13°F
4. a, c, 294 spectators
5. b, d, 7 seconds
6. a, b, 22 snowballs
7. a, d, $\frac{25}{30}$ or $\frac{5}{6}$
8. b, c, 38
9. b, c, d, Barry—63 seconds
10. b, c, 112

page 12

Answers may vary somewhat.
1. the speed of the wind at the bottom
2. fraction that are experts or fraction that are intermediate
3. number of times she fell in the third hour
4. number of passes sold last season
5. price of the boots
6. number of days of the trip
7. number of skiers rescued each day
8. number won by Will or Thomas
9. amount of snow before last night
10. number of collisions on Monday or Tuesday

page 13

1. new $700 snowboard, today is my 14th birthday; *answer is 27*
2. including 3 Flips; *answer is 5*
3. did 3 Backscratchers, 2 Iguana Back Flips, and 5 Nose Rolls; *answer is 3 minutes 20.54 seconds*
4. I've done 200 Ollies; *answer is 4,800*
5. takes 45 minutes to get to the park from home, season pass cost $350; *answer is 3 hours*
6. 1,200 snowboarders, 180 boarders under 12, 70 boarders over 16; *answer is $315*
7. movie tickets cost $6.50 each; *answer is "no"*
8. 37 bruises, 6 cuts, 1 broken finger; *answer is 260*
9. 6 tacos, 2 hot dogs; *answer is 104*

page 14

1. 225
2. 44
3. 1891
4. 10
5. 15
6. 382
7. 3
8. 3,000

page 15

Blue:
1. 183
2. 74
3. 8
4. 100
5. $\frac{1}{4}$
6. 480
7. 80
8. 144

Red:
9. 12,000
10. 10.08

White:
11. $\frac{7}{20}$
12. 20,000
13. 14
14. 0.1
15. $\frac{3}{5}$

Yellow:
16. 6,000
17. 249

Purple:
18. 120
19. 0.8
20. 6
21. 12
22. 20
23. 11.2

Orange:
24. 1,200
25. 4,800

Green—all others
Colored picture shows parachutes.

page 16

1. c; 11$\frac{1}{2}$ miles
2. c; 8 hours
3. b; 52
4. c; 8
5. a; 6
6. a; 16

page 17

Equations may vary in the order in which they are written.
1. n = (42 x 2) + (7 x 3) (*n = 105*)
2. n = 216 ÷ 3 (*n = 72*)
3. n = 400 − 195 (*n = 205 miles*)

4. n = 96 – 28
   (*n = 68 pairs*)
5. n = 7 x 20
   (*n = 140 quarts*)
6. n = 2,224 + 155 +
   2,224 – 350
   (*n = 4,253*)
7. n = $4,500 – $1,850 –
   $570
   (*n = $2,080*)
8. n = .5 x 4,788.5 or
   $\frac{1}{2}$ x 4,788.5
   (*n = 2,394.25 ft or
   2,394$\frac{1}{4}$ ft*)

page 18

Jose—3,200
Abby—3,880
Dylan—4,261
Jessica—4,109
Ryan—4,496
Brad—4,323
Lauren—4,975
Andy—3,495
Alexa—5,000
Denise—4,370
1. Alexa
2. yes

page 19

1. 50%, 6
2. Carla, Josie
3. 9
4. 38
5. Dana, 4
6. 66
7. $\frac{38}{66}$ or $\frac{19}{33}$
8. Josie
9. $\frac{11}{13}$
10. Dana
11. Josie & Carla
12. Patti & Carla

page 20

1. 1 team member gets
   muscles.
2. 1 girl's hair is orange.
3. 1 flower is yellow.
4. 3 hats are green.
5. 7 of the 20 shoes are
   red.
6. 2 shoes are blue.
7. 4 shirts are blue.
8. Half of the rope is red.
9. 1 shirt has stars.
10. 12 of the 20 socks are
    purple.

11. 3 shorts are orange.
12. 1 shirt has stripes.
13. 1 pair of long pants is
    brown.
14. 1 elbow has a bruise.
15. 3 of the 20 knees have
    bandages.
16. 1 team member gets a
    new hat.
17. There is mud under 8
    of the team members.
18. Bees are stinging 2
    team members.
19. Untied shoelaces are
    on 3 shoes.
20. A dog is pulling on the
    shirt of 1 team
    member.

page 21

Answers may vary on 4
and 5.
1. $133.00
2. 630 feet
3. $21.00
4. 11 (plus herself)
5. 4 (plus 1 for Sadie)
6. 80

page 22

Matching pairs are:
5,280 feet—1 mile
   20 qt—5 gal
   54 in.—1$\frac{1}{2}$ yd
   108 in.—3 yd
   4 cups—2 pints
   3$\frac{1}{2}$ lb—56 oz
   3,000 lb—1$\frac{1}{2}$ tons
   2 qt—8 cups
   10 gal—80 pints
   12 feet—4 yards

page 23

Answers may vary
somewhat depending
on exactly where
students measure.
Allow answers in these
ranges:
1. 24–30 cm
2. 18 cm
3. 36 cm
4. 30–36 cm
5. 21–24 cm
6. 24–27 cm
7. 15–18 cm

8. 21–24 cm
9. 48 cm
10. 27 cm
11. 60 cm

page 24

Recipe for 8
6 cups milk
12 eggs
5 bananas
1$\frac{1}{2}$ teaspoons vanilla
1$\frac{1}{3}$ cups protein powder
Recipe for 2
1$\frac{1}{2}$ cups milk
3 eggs
1$\frac{1}{4}$ bananas
$\frac{3}{8}$ teaspoon vanilla
$\frac{1}{3}$ cup protein powder
Recipe for 12
9 cups milk
18 eggs
7$\frac{1}{2}$ bananas
2$\frac{1}{4}$ teaspoons vanilla
2 cups protein powder

page 25

1. Red 7.1
2. Blue 6.35
3. Pink 0.6
4. Black 100.12
5. Yellow 0.36
6. Purple........ 0.09
7. Tan 9.1
8. Orange 14.2
9. Brown 2.05
10. Tan 0.9
11. Silver 0.24
12. Green 0.99
13. Red 10.12
14. Blue........... 8.08
15. Green 9.9
16. Pink 8.8
17. Purple........ 2.4
18. Red 0.009
19. Orange 0.22
20. Yellow....... 3.6
21. Blue........... 0.5
22. Green 50.5
23. Silver 20.5
24. Purple.... 100.2

page 26

Missing numbers in chart:
Biff 4; Bob 18; Ben 5; Bud
   3; Barb 18; Bonnie 0
Totals read 29, 31, 17, 32,
   109

1. 29
2. Ben
3. Biff, Bob, Barb
4. Bonnie
5. Bonnie
6. Bud
7. Ben
8. Biff and Bonnie
9. Twist
10. Straddle
11. Back
12. Straddle
13. Ben
14. Twist
15. Bonnie
16. 109

page 27

1. pizza
2. coffee
3. ice cream
4. hot pretzel
5. nachos
6. pizzas
7. pennant
8. popcorn
9. pretzels
10. drink
11. drinks
12. hot dogs

page 28

1. yes
2. $49.90
3. bridle, blanket,
   breeches
4. $170.80
5. $23.25
6. 2
7. $255.35
8. curry brush
9. bridle and helmet
10. Answers will vary.

page 29

Annie Ace—$5.19
Movin' Marika—$5.55
Daring Donna—$5.45
Suzie Spiker—$4.94
Jumpin' Julie—$9.15
Colleen Cool—$4.34
Towering Tara—$6.04
No-Foul Fran—$8.27
Sally Smasher—$4.95
Nellie Net—$4.70
Sara Server—$8.05
Power Pam—$5.45

page 30
1. D; $25,000
2. S; 351
3. D; 5
4. M; 156
5. A & S (or just S); 35
6. M, A, & S or (M & S); 9
7. A & M; 20
8. A; 8

page 31
1. $17 - 4 + 10 = 23$
2. $4 \times 2 \times 2 = 16$
3. $56 - 6 \div 2 = 25$
4. $\frac{1}{2} + 1 \times 2 = 3$
5. $5 - 2 + 3 = 6$
6. $1 + 2 \times 3 = 9$
7. $8 \times 3 - 4 = 20$
   (or $8 - 3 \times 4 = 20$)
8. $10 \div 2 \times 3 = 15$
   (or $10 \div 2 + 3 = 15$)
9. $20 \times 4 - 80 = 0$
10. $29 + 10 - 13 = 26$
11. $100 \times 100 + 1 = 10,001$
12. $55 - 50 \times 5 = 25$
13. $13 + 13 - 13 = 13$
   (or $13 - 13 + 13 = 13$)
14. $81 \div 9 \times 6 = 54$

page 32
1. P = 39 in.
2. V = 27 in.³
3. V = 87.92 in.³
4. V = 180 in.³
5. V = 1,024 in.³
6. V = 75.36 in.³
7. V = 48 in.³
8. A = 54 in.²
9. P = 6 in.
10. A = 957 in.²
11. A = 4,900 in.²

page 33
1. baseball—8,100 ft²
2. tennis—2,808 ft²
3. boxing—256 ft²
4. swimming 11,108 ft²
5. archery—1,125 ft²
6. wrestling—452.16 ft²
7. track—151,400 ft²
8. sailboat—138 ft²

page 34
1. 75%
2. 10%
3. 20%
4. 90%
5. 25%
6. 80%
7. 50%
8. 40%
9. 5%
10. 30%
11. 55%
12. 15%
13. 90%
14. 75%
15. 10%
16. 25%
17. 30%
18. 40%
19. 80%
20. 50%

page 35
1. 8
2. 72
3. 1
4. 54
5. 18
6. 3
7. 960
8. 24
9. 72
10. 9

page 36
1. 1 hour 5 minutes
2. 9:50 A.M.
3. 11:10 A.M.
4. 1:40 P.M.
5. 20 minutes
6. 5:05 P.M.
7. 30 minutes
8. 7:35 P.M.
9. 10:55 P.M.
10. 8 hours 55 minutes

page 37
1. $24.08
2. sleeveless T-shirt
   (for $19.80)
3. $51.94
4. $85.12
5. $52.43
6. $33.07
7. no
8. $2.10
9. yes
10. $48.16

page 38
1. 30 gal
2. 160 towels
3. 80 cups
4. 40 sticks
5. 3
6. $90
7. 75 pairs
8. $2,800
9. 660

page 39
1. from left to right:
   Tony, Toby, Timothy,
   Terence, Tiny;
   Tiny finished first.
Drawings on 2–5 may vary.
2. Iron Arms
3. Grizzlies
4. Serena
5. Ramon

page 40
Paths should follow these
   numbers:
1. 1—8—160—80—
   trophy 92
2. 2—26—106—212—
   trophy 200
3. 3—45—5—55—
   trophy 11
4. 4—84—74—174—
   trophy 0

page 41
Sunday 10
Monday 440
Tuesday 42
Wednesday 24
Thursday 75 (or 25)
Friday 100
Saturday 56

page 42
Top: The cheese is in
   Carla's locker.
Bottom: Max is in R.J.'s
   locker.

page 43
Problem 1—Jamie is the
   fourth person from the
   front of the line.
Problem 2—One is the
   man with the Tiger's
   flag, and the other is
   the girl second from
   the end.

pages 44–45
Answers will vary. Check
   student equations to
   make sure they add up
   to correct score and to
   make sure they are
   methods that are
   actually possible for
   football scores.

page 46
Answers may vary
   somewhat.
1. yes, b
2. Ted, b
3. 30, b
4. 11, b
5. 66, a
6. 144 square meters, b

page 47
Answers may vary as to
   strategies chosen.
1. yes; mental math or
   estimate
2. 480 feet; write
   equation, estimate, or
   mental math
3. 180; write equation
4. 5:40 P.M.; draw a
   diagram or write
   equation
5. Lucy; draw a diagram
6. 5, 11, 17; trial and error
   or write equation

pages 48–49
Explanations of problem
   solutions will vary.
1. 11
2. Seth
3. $86
4. 864 ft³
5. 15, 18, 9

page 50
Correct answers are
   2, 3, 4, 8, 9, 10, 13, 15